This book belongs to

Daniel

THIS BOOK BELONGS TO:

My Magical Choices

The Magic of Me Series

Copyright @ 2019 Becky Cummings

authorbcummings@gmail.com

ISBN: 978-1-7325963-6-8 (hardcover)
ISBN: 978-1-7325963-7-5 (ebook)

Library of Congress Control Number: 2019907988

Illustrations by Zuzana Svobodová
Book design by Zuzana Svobodová, Maškrtáreň
Editing by Tamara Rittershaus

First printing edition 2019.

Boundless Movement

Visit www.authorbcummings.com

THE MAGIC OF ME
MY MAGICAL CHOICES

WRITTEN BY
BECKY CUMMINGS

ILLUSTRATED BY
ZUZANA SVOBODOVÁ

DEDICATION

To my husband, Jeff, for always supporting me
with my choices so I can do the work
God intended me to do!

TIPS FOR READING WITH CHILDREN

- Have children repeat the positive choice after you.

- Create an action to go with each positive choice. For example, after reading, "I choose to be friendly," make up a special handshake you can do together.

- Ask children to give other examples that show the positive choice in action. For example, after reading the page about responsibility, ask children to share other ways they can show they are responsible.

The choices you make have super powers!

They bring sunshine or rainy showers.

So here are some magical things to do,

that bring the sun to shine right through!

Listen closely to this life advice.

Say, 'I choose' and end with something nice!

Take some action, choose what you do.

Repeat this often, because

MAGIC LIVES IN YOU!

I choose to be responsible!

Bathing, brushing, getting dressed,
now you look and feel your best!
You clean up all the mess you make,
helping out gives mom or dad a break.

I choose to be helpful!

Put toys away and feed the cat,
you might just like a job like that.
Just raise your hand or jump right in,
when helping others, we all win!

I choose to be patient!

Take your time and wait your turn.

Those are tricky things to learn.

When life is slow, you've got to wait.

Stay calm and know

IT TURNS OUT GREAT!

I choose to be confident!

You know you can, you believe in you,

all by yourself, you try something new.

You don't give up when things get rough.

You know you're made to BE SUPER TOUGH!

I choose to be generous!

Giving gifts for
no reason at all,
a cupcake, a flower,
maybe a ball.
Donating books,
clothes, or a toy,
fills your heart
with bursts of joy.

I choose to be calm!

When you're upset, count to ten,
or take a break, then try again.
If still you feel you're sad and blue,
take a calming breath or two.

I choose to be brave!

You speak what's important, kind, and true.

Your heart leads the way and knows what to do.

You try new things with a good attitude.

You do it politely, without being rude!

I choose to be forgiving!

If something makes you feel so sad,

use words to explain the hurt you had.

Then it's okay to let these feelings go.

Heal your heart and let your smile show!

I choose to be a good sport!

Play a game and try to have fun.

Say, "good job" when it's all done!

At times you win, at times you lose,

your attitude is what

YOU CHOOSE!

I choose to be gentle!

Use your hands with grace and care.

Be kind to pets when stroking their hair.

With little friends you're careful too,

nobody wants to get a

BOO-BOO!

I choose to be friendly !

You say hello to new people you meet.

You give high fives or handshakes to greet.

You use kind words with sisters and brothers.

You show respect to fathers and mothers.

I choose to be honest!

Mistakes are part of everyday.

They help you learn a better way.

Just say you're sorry. Make it right.

The truth will make your

HEART FEEL LIGHT.

I choose to be fun!

You play, you dance, you joke, you sing.

You enjoy what each moment may bring.

You do not need to follow the crowd,

be silly, be you and

LAUGH OUT LOUD!

You are the captain of your own ship.

You steer the wheel on this magic trip.

So wisely choose the things you do!

And always remember

MAGIC STARTS IN YOU!

SPECIAL AS CAN BE

THIS IS THE

MAGIC OF ME!

YOUR PICTURE HERE!

Dear Readers,

Thank you for reading *My Magical Choices* to your child or children. I hope that every time this book is read they feel empowered to make positive choices that bring much sunshine to their lives!

If you feel *My Magical Choices* should be shared with others, the best way to help it reach more children is to leave an honest review on Amazon and share it on social media. Your words and photos will help others learn about my book and encourage me to keep on writing!

If you enjoyed this book, be sure to check out book one in this series called *My Magical Words*. It will teach your children to say positive affirmations such as I am loved, I am smart, I am strong and more. Watch their confidence soar as they discover words are important and what they say about themselves matters!

Do you have an older child, age 8 or up? Then grab a copy of *The Magic of Me: A Kid's Spiritual Guide for Health and Happiness.* It contains 30 life-lessons every kid must learn for success in the real world.

I am blessed for your support. Thank you!

With love,

Becky

#themagicofme
#authorbcummings

Becky Cummings is an author, teacher and mom of three. She loves kids and speaking her truth. Becky is blessed to combine these passions by writing children's books that spread messages of love, hope, faith, health, and happiness. When she isn't writing, you might find her salsa dancing, eating a veggie burrito at her favorite Mexican joint, or traveling to new places! Becky is available for author visits and wants to connect with you so be sure to visit her on Facebook fb.me/authorbcummings, or Instagram and visit her website, www.authorbcummings.com.

Zuzana Svobodová is an illustrator. She uses both digital and traditional techniques, as well as the world of fantasy delivered happily by her two children to bring stories to life. When she isn't working on illustrations, she enjoys drawing, doing and teaching yoga, dreaming and baking sweets.